W9-ARK-610

Rookie reader

SPLAT!

Written by
Mary Margaret Pérez-Mercado

Illustrated by
Richard L. Torrey

SCHOLASTIC INC.
New York Toronto London Auckland Sydney
Mexico City New Delhi Hong Kong Buenos Aires

With special love and thanks to my husband, daughters, friends, and family who supported my love of writing.
—M.M.P.-M.

Reading Consultants
Linda Cornwell
Coordinator of School Quality and Professional Improvement
(Indiana State Teachers Association)

Katharine A. Kane
Education Consultant
(Retired, San Diego County Office of Education
and San Diego State University)

ISBN 0-516-23842-6

12 11 10 9 8 7 6   3 4 5 6/0

Printed in the U.S.A.   10

First Scholastic printing, September 2001

I helped my Dad.
We baked a cake.

I think it was a big mistake.

4

The frosting fell.
It hit the floor.

It hit the wall.

It hit the door.

It hit the dog.

It hit the cat.

It hit my Dad
with one big . . .

17

It hit my Mom.

It hit my snake.

But it NEVER EVER hit the cake!

WORD LIST (30 words)

a	fell	never
baked	floor	one
big	frosting	snake
but	helped	splat
cake	hit	the
cat	I	think
dad	it	wall
dog	mistake	was
door	mom	we
ever	my	with

About the Author

Mary Margaret Pérez-Mercado was born and raised in East Los Angeles. She received her B.A. from Cal-State L.A. and her M.L.S. from UCLA. She worked for the Los Angeles County Library System before becoming a youth services librarian for the Tucson-Pima Public Library. She lives with her husband and two daughters in Tucson, Arizona, where they enjoy watching the coyotes, javelinas, roadrunners, and jackrabbits that visit their backyard for drinks of water.

About the Illustrator

Richard L. Torrey has been an illustrator, syndicated cartoonist, and creator of a large line of greeting cards for the past fifteen years. He lives in Shoreham, New York, with his wife, Sue, and his children, Heather, 8, and Drew, 3.